SNOOPY STARS

IN

THE PURSUIT OF PLEASURE

Charles M. Schulz

ℛℛ
RAVETTE BOOKS

Copyright © 1989 United Feature Syndicate, Inc.
All rights reserved

First published by
Ravette Books Limited 1989

This book is sold subject to the condition that
it shall not, by way of trade or otherwise, be
lent, resold, hired out or otherwise circulated
without the publisher's prior consent in any
form of binding or cover other than that in
which this is published and without a similar
condition including this condition being
imposed on the subsequent purchaser.

Printed and bound in Great Britain
for Ravette Books Limited,
3 Glenside Estate, Star Road, Partridge Green,
Horsham, West Sussex RH13 8RA
by Cox & Wyman Ltd, Reading

ISBN 1 85304 146 7

IT'S HARD TO GET AWAY THESE DAYS.. THERE'S JUST SO MUCH TO DO...

Tm Reg U S Pat Off —All rights reserved
© 1970 by United Feature Syndicate, Inc.

OKAY, WHAT SHALL WE READ TONIGHT ..."TREASURE ISLAND"? "HANS BRINKER"?

"THE SIX BUNNY-WUNNIES AND THEIR PONY CART"... AGAIN ?!?

I DON'T UNDERSTAND WHY YOU WANT TO READ THE SAME BOOK EVERY NIGHT... OH, WELL *SIGH* "IT WAS A WARM SPRING DAY, AND THE SIX BUNNY-WUNNIES DECIDED TO GO ON A PICNIC..."

"'I'LL FIX THE LUNCH,' SAID PAM BUNNY-WUNNIE.. 'I'LL HITCH UP OUR PONY,' SAID PETER BUNNY-WUN..."

Tm Reg U S Pat Off — All rights reserved
© 1970 by United Feature Syndicate, Inc.

Tm. Reg. U.S. Pat. Off.—All rights reserved
© 1971 by United Feature Syndicate, Inc.

Tm. Reg U S Pat Off —All rights reserved
© 1972 by United Feature Syndicate, Inc.

4-30

I HOPE I HELPED HIM, BUT I DON'T KNOW...

TEN MINUTES BEFORE YOU GO TO A PARTY IS NO TIME TO BE LEARNING HOW TO DANCE!

Tm. Reg. U.S. Pat. Off.—All rights reserved
© 1973 by United Feature Syndicate, Inc.

"CLOSE DANCING" IS COMING BACK!

THAT'S THE TROUBLE
WITH LIVING IN A
QUIET NEIGHBORHOOD...

I HAVE TO TAKE A BUS ALL
THE WAY DOWNTOWN WHEN
I WANT TO CHASE CARS!

IT'S HARD TO CHEER
UP A DEPRESSED BIRD

HEY, WHAT DO YOU THINK YOU'RE DOING?

© 1979 United Feature Syndicate, Inc.

1979 United Feature Syndicate, Inc.

KAMP OUTT

THAT WASN'T A BAD BREAKFAST

ANY BREAKFAST IS GOOD WHEN YOU'RE STARVING TO DEATH

DO YOU ALWAYS BRING YOUR BROTHER'S DOG TO CAMP?

© 1979 United Feature Syndicate, Inc.

© 1980 United Feature Syndicate, Inc.

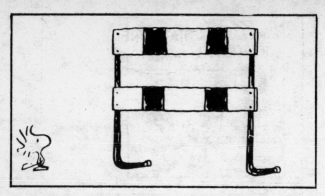

7-12

12-20

© 1981 United Feature Syndicate, Inc.

1983 United Feature Syndicate, Inc.

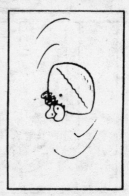

11 6

1964 United Feature Syndicate Inc

MORE STRING!

LET OUT MORE STRING!

© 1985 United Feature Syndicate, Inc.

5-26

© 1985 United Feature Syndicate, Inc.

SO IT'S A HOT DAY... WHY DO YOU HAVE TO SIT IN A BUCKET?

WHY LET THE WHOLE NEIGHBORHOOD KNOW WE DON'T HAVE A POOL?

SOME OF US AREN'T THAT CONCERNED ABOUT OUR IMAGE!

THAT'S TRUE

© 1985 United Feature Syndicate, Inc.

7-19

© 1986 United Feature Syndicate Inc

1-19

© 1986 United Feature Syndicate Inc

THIS IS THE WAY IT WAS MEANT TO BE

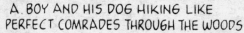

A BOY AND HIS DOG HIKING LIKE PERFECT COMRADES THROUGH THE WOODS

IF YOU SEE A SQUIRREL, OR A DEER, OR A PHEASANT OR A RABBIT, PLEASE FEEL FREE TO BARK AND HOWL AND PURSUE THEM MADLY OVER THE HILLS, THROUGH THE STREAMS AND ACROSS THE FIELDS!

© 1987 United Feature Syndicate, Inc

7-26

© 1961 United Feature Syndicate, Inc.

MOUNTAINS WILL RISE FROM THE SEA!
FIRES WILL RAGE FROM BORDER TO BORDER!
FAMINE WILL DESTROY THE FLOCKS AND HERDS!

KEEP AWAY FROM THIS BLANKET, YOU STUPID BEAGLE, OR YOU AND YOUR KIND WILL REGRET IT FOREVER!

MIDWIVES WILL DESPAIR, AND THERE WILL BE MUCH WEEPING AND WAILING..

5-22

CLOMP! AAUGH!

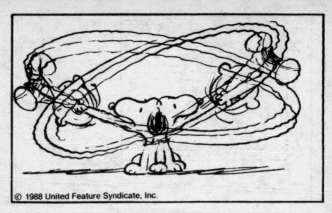

Tm. Reg. U. S. Pat. Off.—All rights reserved
©1966 by United Feature Syndicate, Inc.

Other Snoopy titles published by Ravette Books

Snoopy Stars in this series

No. 1	Snoopy Stars as The Flying Ace	£1.95
No. 2	Snoopy Stars as The Matchmaker	£1.95
No. 3	Snoopy Stars as The Terror of the Ice	£1.95
No. 4	Snoopy Stars as The Legal Beagle	£1.95
No. 5	Snoopy Stars as The Fearless Leader	£1.95
No. 6	Snoopy Stars as Man's Best Friend	£1.95
No. 7	Snoopy Stars as The Sportsman	£1.95
No. 8	Snoopy Stars as The Scourge of The Fairways	£1.95
No. 9	Snoopy Stars as The Branch Manager	£1.95
No. 10	Snoopy Stars as The Literacy Ace	£1.95
No. 11	Snoopy Stars as The Great Pretender	£1.95
No. 12	Snoopy Stars as The Dog-Dish Gourmet	£1.95
No. 13	Snoopy Stars as The Fitness Freak	£1.95
No. 15	Snoopy Stars as The Weatherman	£1.95

Colour landscapes

First Serve	£2.95
Be Prepared	£2.95
Stay Cool	£2.95
Shall We Dance?	£2.95
Let's Go	£2.95
Come Fly With Me	£2.95
Are Magic	£2.95
Hit The Headlines	£2.95

Weekenders

No. 1 Weekender	£4.95

Black and white landscapes

It's a Dog's Life	£2.50
Roundup	£2.50
Freewheelin'	£2.50
Joe Cool	£2.50
Chariots For Hire	£2.50
Dogs Don't Eat Dessert	£2.50
You're on the Wrong Foot Again, Charlie Brown	£2.50
By Supper Possessed	£2.95

All these books are available at your local bookshop or news-agent, or can be ordered direct from the publisher. Just tick the titles you require and fill in the form below. Prices and availability subject to change without notice.

Ravette Books Limited, 3 Glenside Estate, Star Road, Partridge Green, Horsham, West Sussex RH13 8RA

Please send a cheque or postal order, and allow the following for postage and packing. UK: Pocket-books – 45p for one book, 20p for the second book and 15p for each additional book. Other titles – 50p for one book and 30p for each additional book.

Name ....

Address ....

....